Date Due

DATE DUE

MAY 0 1 2004			

Wings of Rhyme

Wings of Rhyme

EDITED BY LLOYD FRANKENBERG

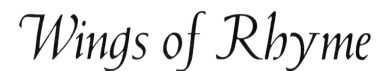

ORNAMENT BY ALAN BENJAMIN

FUNK & WAGNALLS
NEW YORK

Acknowledgment is due to the following Publishers and Author
for permission to reprint copyright poems: for "little tree"
by e. e. cummings, copyright, 1925; renewed, 1953 by E. E.
Cummings. Reprinted from his volume, POEMS 1923-1954, by
permission of Harcourt, Brace & World, Inc.; for "Schoolboys
in Winter" by John Clare, permission is granted by the
Oxford University Press; for "She Moved through the Fair" by
Padraic Colum, permission is granted by the author; for "The
Wind" by James Stephens and "The Lake Isle of Inisfree" by
W. B. Yeats, permission is granted by The Macmillan Company.

Selection and Afterword copyright © 1967
by Lloyd Frankenberg
Published by Funk & Wagnalls, New York
A Division of Reader's Digest Books, Inc.
Library of Congress Catalog Card Number: 67-26043
Designed by Alan Benjamin
Printed in the United States of America

I

Contents

The Book of

Jack and Jill

9

ANONYMOUS

Jack and Jill

Jack and Jill
Went up the Hill,
   To fetch a Pail of Water;
Jack fell down
And broke his Crown,
   And Jill came tumbling after.

10

ANONYMOUS

Little Boy Blue

Little Boy Blue, come blow your horn,
The cow's in the meadow, the sheep in the corn:
But where is the little boy tending the sheep?
He's under the hay-cock fast asleep.
Will you wake him? No, not I,
For if I do, he's sure to cry.

11

ANONYMOUS

Little Jack Horner

Little Jack Horner
Sat in a Corner,
   Eating a Christmas pie;
He put in his Thumb,
And pull'd out a Plum,
   And [said] what a good boy am I.

12

ANONYMOUS

This is the House that Jack Built

This is the house that Jack built.

This is the malt
That lay in the house that Jack built.

This is the rat,
That ate the malt
That lay in the house that Jack built.

This is the cat,
That killed the rat,
That ate the malt
That lay in the house that Jack built.

This is the dog,
That worried the cat,
That killed the rat,
That ate the malt
That lay in the house that Jack built.

This is the cow with the crumpled horn,
That tossed the dog,
That worried the cat,
That killed the rat,
That ate the malt
That lay in the house that Jack built.

This is the maiden all forlorn,
That milked the cow with the crumpled horn,
That tossed the dog,
That worried the cat,
That killed the rat,
That ate the malt
That lay in the house that Jack built.

14

This is the man all tattered and torn,
That kissed the maiden all forlorn,
That milked the cow with the crumpled horn,
That tossed the dog,
That worried the cat,
That killed the rat,
That ate the malt
That lay in the house that Jack built.

This is the priest all shaven and shorn,
That married the man all tattered and torn,
That kissed the maiden all forlorn,
That milked the cow with the crumpled horn,
That tossed the dog,
That worried the cat,
That killed the rat,
That ate the malt
That lay in the house that Jack built.

This is the cock that crowed in the morn,
That waked the priest all shaven and shorn,
That married the man all tattered and torn,
That kissed the maiden all forlorn,
That milked the cow with the crumpled horn,
That tossed the dog,
That worried the cat,
That killed the rat,
That ate the malt
That lay in the house that Jack built.

This is the farmer sowing the corn,
That kept the cock that crowed in the morn,
That waked the priest all shaven and shorn,
That married the man all tattered and torn,
That kissed the maiden all forlorn,
That milked the cow with the crumpled horn,
That tossed the dog,
That worried the cat,
That killed the rat,
That ate the malt
That lay in the house that Jack built.

16

ANONYMOUS

Sing a Song of Sixpence

Sing a song of sixpence,
A pocket full of rye,
Four and twenty blackbirds,
Bak'd in a pie.

When the pie was opened,
The birds began to sing;
Was not that a dainty dish,
To set before the king?

17

ANONYMOUS

Hickory Dickory Dock

Hickory, Dickory Dock
A Mouse ran up the Clock,
The Clock Struck One,
The Mouse fell down,
Hickory Dickory Dock.

18

ANONYMOUS

Simple Simon

Simple Simon met a pieman,
    Going to the fair;
Said Simple Simon to the pieman,
    Let me taste your ware.

Said the pieman unto Simon,
    Show me first your penny;
Said Simple Simon to the pieman,
    Indeed I have not any.

Simple Simon went a-fishing,
    For to catch a whale;
All the water he had got
    Was in his mother's pail.

Simple Simon went to look
    If plums grew on a thistle;
He pricked his finger very much,
    Which made poor Simon whistle.

19

ANONYMOUS

Little Bo-peep

Little Bo-peep
Has lost her sheep
   And doesn't know where to find them.
Leave them alone
And they'll come home
   Wagging their tails behind them.

20

ANONYMOUS

There was an old woman who lived in a shoe

There was an old woman who lived in a shoe,
She had so many children she didn't know what to do,
She gave them some broth without any bread;
She whipped them all soundly and put them to bed.

21

ANONYMOUS

Old Mother Hubbard

Old Mother Hubbard
Went to the cupboard,
To fetch her poor dog a bone;
But when she came there
The cupboard was bare
And so the poor dog had none.

22

ANONYMOUS

Doctor Foster

Doctor Foster
Went to Gloucester
All in a shower of rain;
He stepped in a puddle,
Right up to his middle,
And never went there again.

23

ANONYMOUS

Tweedledum and Tweedledee

Tweedledum and Tweedlede
   Agreed to fight a battle,
For Tweedledum said Tweedledee
   Had spoiled his nice new rattle.
Just then flew by a monstrous crow,
   As black as a tar-barrel,
Which frightened both the heroes so,
   They quite forgot their quarrel.

24

ANONYMOUS

There was a crooked man

There was a crooked man, and he walked a crooked mile,
He found a crooked sixpence against a crooked stile;
He bought a crooked cat, which caught a crooked mouse,
And they all lived together in a little crooked house.

25

ANONYMOUS

Mary had a little lamb

Mary had a little lamb,
   Its fleece was white as snow;
And everywhere that Mary went
   The lamb was sure to go.

It followed her to school one day,
   That was against the rule;
It made the children laugh and play,
   To see a lamb in school.

And so the teacher turned it out,
   But still it lingered near,
And waited patiently about
   Till Mary did appear.

Why does the lamb love Mary so?
   The eager children cry;
Why, Mary loves the lamb, you know,
   The teacher did reply.

26

ANONYMOUS

There was a little woman

There was a little woman, as I have heard tell,
She went to market her eggs for to sell;
She went to market all on a market day
And she fell asleep on the king's highway.

There came by a peddler, his name was Stout,
He cut her petticoats all round about;
He cut her petticoats up to her knees
Which made the little woman to shiver and sneeze.

When this little woman began to awake,
She began to shiver, and she began to shake;
She began to shake, and she began to cry,
"Lawk a mercy on me, this is none of I!

27

"But if this be I, as I do hope it be,
I have a little dog at home and he knows me;
If it be I, he'll wag his little tail,
And if it be not I, he'll loudly bark and wail."

Home went the little woman all in the dark,
Up starts the little dog, and he began to bark;
He began to bark and she began to cry,
"Lawk a mercy on me, this is none of I!"

28

H. W. LONGFELLOW

There Was a Little Girl

There was a little girl,
And she had a little curl
   Right in the middle of her forehead.
When she was good
She was very, very good,
   And when she was bad she was horrid.

One day she went upstairs,
When her parents, unawares,
   In the kitchen were occupied with meals
And she stood upon her head
In her little trundle-bed,
   And then began hooraying with her heels.

Her mother heard the noise,
And she thought it was the boys
   A-playing at a combat in the attic;
But when she climbed the stair,
And found Jemima there,
   She took and she did spank her most emphatic.

29

ANONYMOUS

Georgie Porgie

Georgie Porgie, pudding and pie,
Kissed the girls and made them cry;
When the boys came out to play,
Georgie Porgie ran away.

30

ANONYMOUS

Ride a Cock-horse

Ride a cock-horse to Banbury Cross,
To see a fine lady upon a white horse;
Rings on her fingers and bells on her toes,
She shall have music wherever she goes.

31

ANONYMOUS

There once were two cats of Kilkenny

There once were two cats of Kilkenny,
Each thought there was one cat too many,
So they fought and they fit,
And they scratched and they bit,
Till, excepting their nails
And the tips of their tails,
Instead of two cats, there weren't any.

32

ANONYMOUS

Humpty-Dumpty

Humpty-Dumpty sat on a wall,
Humpty-Dumpty had a great fall.
All the king's horses, and all the king's men,
Couldn't put Humpty together again.

33

ANONYMOUS

Old King Cole

Old King Cole
Was a merry old soul,
And a merry old soul was he;
He called for his pipe,
And he called for his bowl,
And he called for his fiddlers three.

Every fiddler, he had a fiddle,
And a very fine fiddle had he;
Twee tweedle dee, tweedle dee, went the fiddlers.
Oh there's none so rare
As can compare
With King Cole and his fiddlers three.

ROBERT LOUIS STEVENSON

Bed in Summer

In winter I get up at night
And dress by yellow candle-light.
In summer, quite the other way,
I have to go to bed by day.

I have to go to bed and see
The birds still hopping on the tree,
Or hear the grown-up people's feet
Still going past me in the street.

And does it not seem hard to you,
When all the sky is clear and blue,
And I should like so much to play,
To have to go to bed by day?

ANONYMOUS

Three young rats

Three young rats with black felt hats,
Three young ducks with new straw flats,
Three young dogs with curling tails,
Three young cats with demi-veils,
Went out to walk with two young pigs
In satin vests and sorrel wigs.
But suddenly it chanced to rain
And so they all went home again.

The Book of

the Runcible Spoon

EDWARD LEAR

The Owl and the Pussycat

The Owl and the Pussycat went to sea
   In a beautiful pea-green boat:
They took some honey, and plenty of money
   Wrapped up in a five-pound note.
The Owl looked up to the stars above,
   And sang to a small guitar,
"Oh, lovely Pussy, oh, Pussy, my love,
   What a beautiful Pussy you are,
         You are,
         You are!
   What a beautiful Pussy you are!"

40

Pussy said to the Owl, "You elegant fowl,
  How charmingly sweet you sing!
Oh, let us be married; too long we have tarried:
  But what shall we do for a ring?"
They sailed away for a year and a day,
  To the land where the bong-tree grows;
And there in the wood a Piggy-wig stood,
  With a ring at the end of his nose,
        His nose,
        His nose,
  With a ring at the end of his nose.

"Dear Pig, are you willing to sell for one shilling
  Your ring?" Said the Piggy, "I will."
So they took it away and were married next day
  By the Turkey who lives on the hill.
They dined on mince and slices of quince,
  Which they ate with a runcible spoon;
And hand in hand, on the edge of the sand,
  They danced by the light of the moon,
        The moon,
        The moon,
  They danced by the light of the moon.

41

EDWARD LEAR

There was an old man of Thermopylae

There was an old man of Thermopylae,
Who never did anything properly;
   But they said: "If you choose
   To boil eggs in your shoes,
You cannot remain in Thermopylae."

42

EDWARD LEAR

There was an old man who said Hush

There was an old man who said, "Hush!
I perceive a young bird in this bush!"
    When they said, "Is it small?"
    He replied, "Not at all;
It is four times as big as the bush!"

43

EDWARD LEAR

There was once a man with a beard

There was once a man with a beard
Who said, "It is just as I feared!—
    Two Owls and a Hen,
    Four Larks and a Wren
Have all built their nests in my beard."

44

ANTHONY EUWER

As a beauty I am not a star

As a beauty I am not a star,
There are others more handsome by far.
   But my face I don't mind it,
   For I am behind it.
It's the people in front get the jar.

45

GELETT BURGESS

I wish that my room had a floor

I wish that my room had a floor.
I don't so much care for a door;
 But this walking around
 Without touching the ground
Is getting to be quite a bore.

GELETT BURGESS

The Purple Cow

I never saw a Purple Cow,
    I never hope to see one;
But I can tell you, anyhow,
    I'd rather see than be one.

47

ANONYMOUS

There was a young lady of Niger

There was a young lady of Niger
Who smiled as she rode on a tiger.
  They came back from the ride
  With the lady inside
And the smile on the face of the tiger.

48

ANONYMOUS

There was a young maid who said why

There was a young maid who said, "Why
Can't I look in my ear with my eye?
   If I give my mind to it,
   I'm sure I can do it,
You never can tell till you try."

49

OLIVER GOLDSMITH

An Elegy on the Death
of a Mad Dog

Good people all, of every sort,
   Give ear unto my song;
And if you find it wondrous short,—
   It cannot hold you long.

In Islington there was a man,
   Of whom the world might say
That still a godly race he ran,—
   Whene'er he went to pray.

A kind and gentle heart he had,
   To comfort friends and foes;
The naked every day he clad,—
   When he put on his clothes.

And in that town a dog was found,
   As many dogs there be,
Both mongrel, puppy, whelp, and hound,
   And curs of low degree.

50

The dog and man at first were friends;
　But when a pique began,
The dog, to gain some private ends,
　Went mad, and bit the man.

Around from all the neighboring streets,
　The wondering neighbors ran,
And swore the dog had lost its wits
　To bite so good a man.

The wound it seemed both sore and sad
　To every Christian eye;
And while they swore the dog was mad
　They swore the man would die.

But soon a wonder came to light,
　That showed the rogues they lied;
The man recovered of the bite,
　The dog it was that died.

51

DR. JOHNSON

If a man who turnips cries

If a man who turnips cries,
Cry not when his father dies,
'T is a proof that he would rather
Have a turnip than a father.

52

ANONYMOUS

There was an old man of Peru

There was an old man of Peru
Who dreamt he was eating his shoe.
   He awoke in a fright
   In the middle of the night
And found it was perfectly true.

53

ANONYMOUS

A Case

As I was going up the stair
I met a man who wasn't there.
He wasn't there again today—
I wish to God he'd go away.

54

ANONYMOUS

Two little men with equal feet

Two little men with equal feet
Down the stairs and up the street;
Down the street and up the stairs
Two little equal early bears.

55

ANONYMOUS

Relativity

There was a young lady named Bright,
Who travelled much faster than light.
   She started one day
   In the relative way,
And returned on the previous night.

LEWIS CARROLL

How doth the little crocodile?

How doth the little crocodile
    Improve his shining tail,
And pour the waters of the Nile
    On every golden scale!

How cheerfully he seems to grin,
    How neatly spreads his claws,
And welcomes little fishes in,
    With gently smiling jaws!

LEWIS CARROLL

"You are old, father William"

"You are old, father William," the young man said,
  "And your hair has become very white;
And yet you incessantly stand on your head—
  Do you think, at your age, it is right?"

"In my youth," father William replied to his son,
  "I feared it might injure the brain;
But, now that I'm perfectly sure I have none,
  Why, I do it again and again."

"You are old," said the youth, "as I mentioned before,
  And have grown most uncommonly fat;
Yet you turned a back-somersault in at the door—
  Pray what is the reason of that?"

"In my youth," said the sage, as he shook his grey locks,
  "I kept all my limbs very supple
By the use of this ointment—one shilling the box—
  Allow me to sell you a couple?"

58

"You are old," said the youth, "and your jaws are too weak
  For anything tougher than suet;
Yet you finished the goose, with the bones and the beak—
  Pray, how did you manage to do it?"

"In my youth," said his father, "I took to the law,
  And argued each case with my wife;
And the muscular strength, which it gave to my jaw,
  Has lasted the rest of my life."

"You are old," said the youth, "one would hardly suppose
  That your eye was as steady as ever;
Yet you balanced an eel on the end of your nose—
  What made you so awfully clever?"

"I have answered three questions, and that is enough,"
  Said his father. "Don't give yourself airs!
Do you think I can listen all day to such stuff?
  Be off, or I'll kick you down stairs!"

59

LEWIS CARROLL

The Walrus and the Carpenter

The sun was shining on the sea,
    Shining with all his might:
He did his very best to make
    The billows smooth and bright—
And this was odd, because it was
    The middle of the night.

The moon was shining sulkily,
    Because she thought the sun
Had no business to be there
    After the day was done—
'It's very rude of him,' she said,
    'To come and spoil the fun!'

The sea was wet as wet could be,
    The sands were dry as dry.
You could not see a cloud, because
    No cloud was in the sky:
No birds were flying overhead—
    There were no birds to fly.

The Walrus and the Carpenter
   Were walking close at hand:
They wept like anything to see
   Such quantities of sand:
'If this were only cleared away,'
   They said, 'it would be grand!'

'If seven maids with seven mops
   Swept it for half a year,
Do you suppose,' the Walrus said,
   'That they could get it clear?'
'I doubt it,' said the Carpenter,
   And shed a bitter tear.

'O Oysters, come and walk with us!'
   The Walrus did beseech.
'A pleasant walk, a pleasant talk,
   Along the briny beach:
We cannot do with more than four,
   To give a hand to each.'

The eldest Oyster looked at him,
   But never a word he said:
The eldest Oyster winked his eye,
   And shook his heavy head—
Meaning to say he did not choose
   To leave the oyster-bed.

61

But four young Oysters hurried up,
　All eager for the treat:
Their coats were brushed, their faces washed,
　Their shoes were clean and neat—
And this was odd, because, you know,
　They hadn't any feet.

Four other Oysters followed them,
　And yet another four;
And thick and fast they came at last,
　And more, and more, and more—
All hopping through the frothy waves,
　And scrambling to the shore.

The Walrus and the Carpenter
　Walked on a mile or so,
And then they rested on a rock
　Conveniently low:
And all the little Oysters stood
　And waited in a row.

'The time has come,' the Walrus said,
　'To talk of many things:
Of shoes—and ships—and sealing-wax—
　Of cabbages—and kings—
And why the sea is boiling hot—
　And whether pigs have wings.'

'But wait a bit,' the Oysters cried,
    'Before we have our chat;
For some of us are out of breath,
    And all of us are fat!'
'No hurry!' said the Carpenter.
    They thanked him much for that.

'A loaf of bread,' the Walrus said,
    'Is what we chiefly need:
Pepper and vinegar besides
    Are very good indeed—
Now, if you're ready, Oysters dear,
    We can begin to feed.'

'But not on us!' the Oysters cried,
    Turning a little blue.
'After such kindness, that would be
    A dismal thing to do!'
'The night is fine,' the Walrus said.
    'Do you admire the view?

'It was so kind of you to come!
    And you are very nice!'
The Carpenter said nothing but
    'Cut us another slice.
I wish you were not quite so deaf—
    I've had to ask you twice!'

'It seems a shame,' the Walrus said,
　'To play them such a trick
After we've brought them out so far,
　And made them trot so quick!'
The Carpenter said nothing but
　'The butter's spread too thick!'

'I weep for you,' the Walrus said:
　'I deeply sympathize.'
With sobs and tears he sorted out
　Those of the largest size,
Holding his pocket-handkerchief
　Before his streaming eyes.

'O Oysters,' said the Carpenter,
　'You've had a pleasant run!
Shall we be trotting home again?'
　But answer came there none—
And this was scarcely odd, because
　They'd eaten every one.

LEWIS CARROLL

Jabberwocky

'Twas brillig, and the slithy toves
    Did gyre and gimble in the wabe;
All mimsy were the borogoves,
    And the mome raths outgrabe.

"Beware the Jabberwock, my son!
    The jaws that bite, the claws that catch!
Beware the Jubjub bird, and shun
    The frumious Bandersnatch!"

He took his vorpal sword in hand:
    Long time the manxome foe he sought.
So rested he by the Tumtum tree,
    And stood awhile in thought.

And as in uffish thought he stood,
    The Jabberwork, with eyes of flame,
Came whiffling through the tulgey wood,
    And burbled as it came!

65

One, two! One, two! And through, and through
   The vorpal blade went snicker-snack!
He left it dead, and with its head
   He went galumphing back.

"And hast thou slain the Jabberwock?
   Come to my arms, my beamish boy!
Oh, frabjous day! Callooh! callay!"
   He chortled in his joy.

'Twas brillig, and the slithy toves
   Did gyre and gimble in the wabe;
All mimsy were the borogoves
   And the mome raths outgrabe.

The Book of

the Shoes of Wonder

JOHN KEATS

A Song about Myself

There was a naughty boy,
   A naughty boy was he,
He would not stop at home,
   He could not quiet be—
      He took
      In his knapsack
      A book
      Full of vowels
      And a shirt
      With some towels—
      A slight cap
      For night cap—
      A hair brush,
      Comb ditto,
      New stockings
      For old ones
      Would split O!
      This knapsack
      Tight at's back

He rivetted close
And followed his nose
  To the north,
  To the north,
And followed his nose to the north.

There was a naughty boy,
  And a naughty boy was he,
For nothing would he do
  But scribble poetry—
    He took
    An ink stand
    In his hand
    And a pen
    Big as ten
    In the other
    And away
    In a pother
    He ran
    To the mountains
    And fountains
    And ghostes
    And postes
    And witches
    And ditches

71

And wrote
In his coat
When the weather
Was cool,
Fear of gout,
And without
When the weather
Was warm—
Och, the charm
When we choose
To follow one's nose
To the north,
To the north,
To follow one's nose to the north!

There was a naughty boy
And a naughty boy was he,
He kept little fishes
In washing tubs three
In spite
Of the might
Of the maid
Nor afraid
Of his Granny-good
He often would

Hurly burly
Get up early
And go
By hook or crook
To the brook
And bring home
Miller's thumb,
Tittlebat
Not over fat,
Minnows small
As the stall
Of a glove,
Not above
The size
Of a nice
Little baby's
Little fingers—
O he made
'Twas his trade
Of fish a pretty kettle
A kettle
A kettle
Of fish a pretty kettle
A kettle!

73

There was a naughty boy
    And a naughty boy was he,
He ran away to Scotland
    The people for to see—
        Then he found
        That the ground
        Was as hard,
        That a yard
        Was as long,
        That a song
        Was as merry,
        That a cherry
        Was as red,
        That lead
        Was as weighty,
        That fourscore
        Was as eighty,
        That a door
        Was as wooden
        As in England—
So he stood in
    His shoes and he wondered,
    He wondered,
He stood in
    His shoes and he wondered.

74

ANONYMOUS

Sumer is icumen in

Sumer is icumen in,
   Lhude sing cuccu;
Groweth sed and bloweth med,
   And springeth the wude nu.
     Sing cuccu!

Awe bleteth after lomb,
   Lhouth after calve cu;
Bulluc sterteth, bucke verteth,
   Murie sing cuccu.

Cuccu, cuccu, wel singes thu, cuccu:
   Na swike thu naver nu;
Sing cuccu, nu, sing cuccu,
   Sing cuccu, sing cuccu, nu!

75

Summer is a-coming in,
   Loudly sing cuckoo;
Groweth seed and bloweth mead
   And springeth the wood anew.
Sing cuckoo!

Ewe a-bleateth after lamb,
   Loweth after calf the cow;
Bullock starteth, buck averteth,
   Merrily sing cuckoo!

Cuckoo, cuckoo, well singest thou, cuckoo:
   Nor cease thou never now;
Sing cuckoo, now, sing cuckoo,
   Sing cuckoo, sing cuckoo, now!

WILLIAM ALLINGHAM

The Fairy Folk

Up the airy mountain,
   Down the rushy glen
We daren't go a-hunting,
   For fear of little men;
Wee folk, good folk,
   Trooping all together;
Green jacket, red cap,
   And white owl's feather.

Down along the rocky shore
   Some make their home,
They live on crispy pancakes
   Of yellow tide-foam;
Some in the reeds
   Of the black mountain-lake,
With frogs for their watch-dogs,
   All night awake.

High on the hill-top
   The old King sits;
He is now so old and gray
   He's nigh lost his wits.
With a bridge of white mist
   Columbkill he crosses,
On his stately journeys
   From Slieveleague to Rosses;

Or going up with music,
   On cold starry nights,
To sup with the Queen
   Of the gay Northern Lights.

They stole little Bridget
   For seven years long;
When she came down again
   Her friends were all gone.
They took her lightly back,
   Between the night and the morrow;
They thought that she was fast asleep,
   But she was dead with sorrow.
They have kept her ever since
   Deep within the lakes,
On a bed of flag leaves,
   Watching till she wakes.

78

By the craggy hillside,
    Through the mosses bare,
They have planted thorn-trees
    For pleasure here and there.
Is any man so daring
    As dig one up in spite?
He shall find the thornies set
    In his bed at night.

Up the airy mountain,
    Down the rushy glen,
We daren't go a-hunting
    For fear of little men;
Wee folk, good folk,
    Trooping all together;
Green jacket, red cap,
    And white owl's feather.

W. B. YEATS

The Lake Isle of Innisfree

I will arise and go now, and go to Innisfree,
And a small cabin build there, of clay and wattles made:
Nine bean-rows will I have there, a hive for the honeybee,
And live alone in the bee-loud glade.

And I shall have some peace there, for peace comes
                              dropping slow,
Dropping from the veils of the morning to where the
                              cricket sings;
There midnight's all a glimmer, and noon a purple glow,
And evening full of the linnet's wings.

I will arise and go now, for always night and day
I hear lake water lapping with low sounds by the shore;
While I stand on the roadway, or on the pavements grey,
I hear it in the deep heart's core.

THOMAS BAILEY ALDRICH

Memory

My mind lets go a thousand things,
Like dates of wars and deaths of kings,
And yet recalls the very hour—
'Twas noon by yonder village tower,
And on the last blue noon in May
The wind came briskly up this way,
Crisping the brook beside the road;
Then, pausing here, set down its load
Of pine-scents, and shook listlessly
Two petals from that wild-rose tree.

JAMES STEPHENS

The Wind

The wind stood up, and gave a shout;
He whistled on his fingers, and

Kicked the withered leaves about,
And thumped the branches with his hand,

And said he'd kill, and kill, and kill;
And so he will! And so he will!

JOHN CLARE

Schoolboys in Winter

The schoolboys still their morning rambles take
To neighboring village school with playing speed,
Loitering with pastime's leisure till they quake;
Oft looking up the wild-geese droves to heed,
Watching the letters which their journeys make,
Or plucking haws on which the fieldfares feed,
And hips, and sloes! and on each shallow lake
Making glib slides, where they like shadows go
Till some fresh pastimes in their minds awake.
Then off they start anew and hasty blow
Their numbed and clumpsing fingers till they glow;
Then races with their shadows wildly run
That stride huge giants o'er the shining snow
In the pale splendor of the winter sun.

83

PADRAIC COLUM

She moved through the fair

My young love said to me, "My brothers won't mind,
And my parents won't slight you for your lack of kind."
Then she stepped away from me, and this she did say
"It will not be long, love, till our wedding day."

She stepped away from me and she moved through the fair,
And I fondly watched her go here and go there,
Till she went her way homeward with one star awake,
As the swan in the evening moves over the lake.

The people were saying no two were ere wed
But one had a sorrow that never was said,
And I smiled as she passed with her goods and her gear,
And that was the last that I saw of my dear.

I dreamed it last night that my young love came in,
So softly she entered, her feet made no din;
She came close beside me, and this she did say
"It will not be long, love, till our wedding day."

EDGAR ALLAN POE

To Helen

Helen, thy beauty is to me
   Like those Nicaean barks of yore,
That gently, o'er a perfumed sea,
   The weary, wayworn wanderer bore
   To his own native shore.

On desperate seas long wont to roam,
   Thy hyacinth hair, thy classic face,
Thy Naiad airs have brought me home
   To the glory that was Greece
   And the grandeur that was Rome.

Lo! in yon brilliant window-niche
   How statue-like I see thee stand,
The agate lamp within thy hand!
   Ah, Psyche, from the regions which
   Are Holy Land!

ALFRED, LORD TENNYSON

Flower in the crannied wall

Flower in the crannied wall,
I pluck you out of the crannies,
I hold you here, root and all, in my hand,
Little flower—but *if* I could understand
What you are, root and all, and all in all,
I should know what God and man is.

86

WILLIAM SHAKESPEARE

Full Fathom Five

Ariel: Full fathom five thy father lies;
              Of his bones are coral made;
          Those are pearls that were his eyes:
              Nothing of him that doth fade
          But doth suffer a sea-change
          Into something rich and strange.
          Sea-nymphs hourly ring his knell:
Refrain.   Ding-dong.
          Hark! now I hear them,—ding-dong, bell.

WILLIAM SHAKESPEARE

Come unto these yellow sands

Ariel :   Come unto these yellow sands,
               And then take hands.
           Curtsied when you have, and kiss'd
               The wild waves whist,
           Foot it featly here and there,
           And, sweet sprites, the burden bear.

Refrain (dispersedly).   Hark, hark!
                                   Bow-wow.
           The watch-dogs bark!
                                   Bow-wow.

Ariel.   Hark, hark! I hear
           The strain of strutting chanticleer
           Cry, "Cock-a-diddle-dow."

GERARD MANLEY HOPKINS

Inversnaid

This darksome burn, horseback brown,
His rollrock highroad roaring down,
In coop and in comb the fleece of his foam
Flutes and low to the lake falls home.

A windpuff-bonnet of fáwn-fróth
Turns and twindles over the broth
Of a pool so pitchblack, féll-frówning,
It rounds and rounds Despair to drowning.

Degged with dew, dappled with dew
Are the groins of the braes that the brook treads through,
Wiry heathpacks, flitches of fern,
And the beadbonny ash that sits over the burn.

What would the world be, once bereft
Of wet and of wildness? Let them be left,
O let them be left, wildness and wet;
Long live the weeds and the wilderness yet.

89

e. e. cummings

little tree

little tree
little silent Christmas tree
you are so little
you are more like a flower

who found you in the green forest
and were you very sorry to come away?
see i will comfort you
because you smell so sweetly

i will kiss your cool bark
and hug you safe and tight
just as your mother would,
only don't be afraid

look   the spangles
that sleep all the year in a dark box
dreaming of being taken out and allowed to shine,
the balls the chains red and gold the fluffy threads,

90

put up your little arms
and i'll give them all to you to hold
every finger shall have its ring
and there won't be a single place dark or unhappy

then when you're quite dressed
you'll stand in the window for everyone to see
and how they'll stare!
oh but you'll be very proud

and my little sister and i will take hands
and looking up at our beautiful tree
we'll dance and sing
"Noel Noel"

91

ROBERT HERRICK

Another Grace for a Child

Here a little child I stand,
Heaving up my either hand;
Cold as paddocks though they be,
Here I lift them up to Thee,
For a benison to fall
On our meat and on us all. Amen.

A word about reading

To a child, a second language is apt to come rather easily, simply by hearing it spoken. American children brought up in Europe often have two native tongues. In the beginning, at least, they scarcely need to study either.

Learning comes later, when we have gotten beyond the stage of direct imitation. The later we begin, the more deliberate the effort becomes. What is at first a transition turns into translation. A second language is then truly foreign. Even the act of pursing the lips to make a French "u" may make us feel self-conscious.

So too with poetry, which may also be thought of as a second language. Not that its words are necessarily different from the words we use in talking. The important difference lies more in how the words are put together.

Rather than following each other hit-or-miss, as if by accident, they make patterns, more or less regular recurrences of sound and rhythm: "Little Jack Horner / Sat in a corner." The rhymes and repetitions of Mother Goose rhymes tend to be very definite and pronounced: "Little Bo-peep / Has lost her sheep." Children enjoy a strong beat, like the game of bouncing a ball, or of taking so many steps in a square.

Later they may come to respond to more subtle variations: "Flower in the crannied wall, / I pluck you out of the crannies," or "little tree / little silent Christmas tree."

Clear, definite rhythms generally go with clear, definite meanings. Children can easily picture little Jack Horner sitting in his corner, and are not troubled by the fact that Jack may not exist. To a child, there is little separation between the real and the fictitious. It is, again, later that we get to be disturbed by this difference, to become distrustful of the imagination.

"You're nothing but a pack of cards!" says Alice as she is about to wake up from her dream of Wonderland. Nearly all of us undergo this shock at the cleavage between the imaginary and the real. Even if the "real"—Lewis Carroll's twist—is a pack of cards.

Alice has had so many rhymes read to her, she has believed in so many implausible happenings, that you feel the shock will not last for long. True, she now knows that what she took for real was "only a dream." But "only a dream" is part of reality, too, as poetry is part of life. What we know and what we don't know are alike magical. The translation from one to the other enhances both. Each possesses a strangeness; each is another language, forever new.

When better to learn this, without even learning it, than in childhood? The poems heard and repeated and remembered are not only a pleasure in themselves. Like pebbles dropped in a pool, they lead to ever-widening circles of delight.

Lloyd Frankenberg

First Line Index

This darksome burn, horseback brown, 88
This is the house that Jack built, 12
Three young rats with black felt hats, 35
'Twas brillig, and the slithy toves, 64
Tweedledum and Tweedledee, 23
Two little men with equal feet, 54
Up the airy mountain, 76
"You are old, father William," the young man said, 57

Authors' Index